- These student worksheets are intended to complement the corresponding revision guide to help to reinforce your understanding and improve your confidence.

- Every worksheet is cross-referenced to 'The Essentials of GCSE Design and Technology: Electronic Products' written by David McHugh.

- The questions concentrate purely on the content you need to cover, and the limited space forces you to choose and word your answer carefully.

These worksheets can be used as...
- classwork sheets where pupils use the revision guide to answer the questions
- harder classwork sheets where pupils study the topic first, then answer the questions without the guide
- easy-to-mark homework sheets to test pupils' understanding and reinforce their learning
- the basis for learning homeworks which are then tested in subsequent lessons
- test material for topics
- a structured revision programme prior to the exam.

- Remember to enter your score at the bottom of each page in the small grey box [ ], and also to put your score in the marks column on the contents page.

WRITTEN BY: DAVID McHUGH

WITHDRAWN

Chief Examiner and Principal Moderator for GCSE Design and Technology Electronic Products and a leading trainer for teacher INSET meetings and courses.

MANY THANKS TO: Rapid Electronics for supplying the images of the components.

• CONTENTS

New College Nottingham

CONTENTS

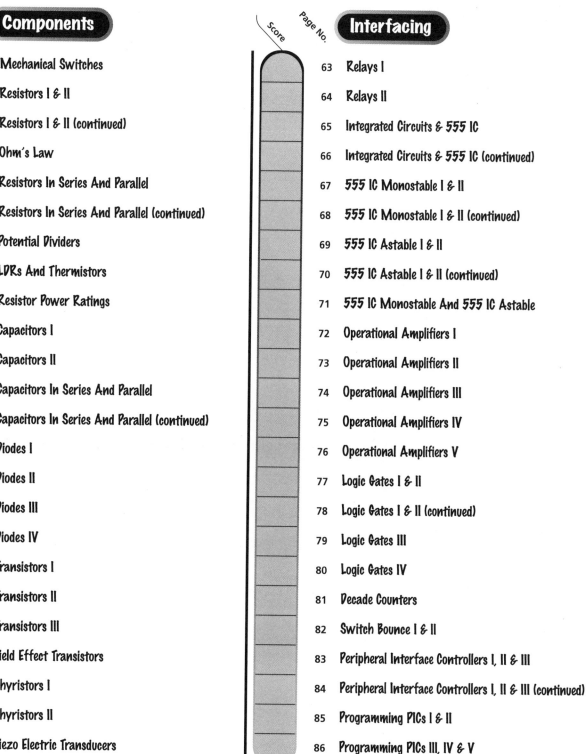

1. What is a) the name and b) the website address of your awarding body?

a) ....   b) ....

The Written Paper

2. Find out the following from your teacher:

a) The date of your mock exam. ....

b) The date of your Year 11 written exam. ....

c) The percentage of the total mark that the written exam is worth. ....

3. Name FIVE areas that could come up in the written exam.

i) ....   ii) ....

iii) ....   iv) ....

v) ....

The Coursework Project

4. What is the ideal weighting of Electronics and Resistant Materials in your coursework project?

....

5. Ask your teacher when the deadline is for your coursework project.

....

6. What percentage of the total mark is your coursework project worth?

....

7. How much time should you spend on...

a) your project in total? ....

b) designing your electronic product? ....

c) making your electronic product? ....

8. How should you aim to split your time between the electronics and the resistant materials part of your coursework project?

....

9. Why is the quality of your written communication important?

....

1. Unscramble the words below that describe things which should be included in your design folder.

SEDING FRIBE ....

CHARSEER ....

SLAINSAY ....

FICTIONISPACE ....

TAILINI SADIE ....

POTMENDELVE ....

LIFAN SINGED SPARPOOL ....

STIGENT DAN ONUVALITEA ....

TYQUAIL SUNCAREAS ....

2. There are **ELEVEN** items in the grid below related to the stages in the design process in industry. Write the words in the space below the grid when you find them.

D	I	P	W	R	J	K	A	M	R	U	X	P	L	A
P	E	K	I	G	D	A	X	V	N	C	K	O	T	M
L	O	V	R	A	S	E	R	Y	E	L	K	Q	C	M
A	E	D	E	S	I	G	N	B	R	I	E	F	U	O
N	E	P	S	L	Z	I	R	Y	D	E	M	N	D	Y
O	T	Z	E	K	O	B	M	E	P	N	B	E	O	A
F	C	T	A	Y	D	P	N	C	R	T	B	C	R	W
M	U	Z	R	W	J	R	T	T	O	R	X	M	P	V
A	X	D	C	T	K	O	G	H	R	A	D	C	E	R
N	I	O	H	L	I	B	B	M	E	Z	W	O	H	U
U	N	M	A	N	A	L	Y	S	E	I	D	G	T	A
F	I	M	U	N	Z	E	S	T	B	N	D	P	E	S
A	N	T	R	O	C	M	N	A	B	Q	U	E	K	A
C	G	D	E	S	I	G	N	I	D	E	A	S	A	T
T	O	R	R	T	Y	U	A	S	F	R	P	V	M	P
U	R	G	Y	A	T	E	S	T	D	U	N	M	C	O
R	O	N	B	C	E	A	G	H	J	I	A	T	N	P
E	V	A	L	U	A	T	E	B	R	U	W	O	P	G

....

....

....

....

....

....

....

....

1. How should you start your project?

2. Try to come up with a brief for an electronic product which uses a timing device.

3. Listed below are some ideas for electronic products.

- A money box which outputs a reward each time a coin is inserted.
- An electronic die.
- An electronic device to help darts players keep score.

Choose ONE of the ideas and create a brief for it by filling in the various headings below:

a) Purpose of product

b) Target users

c) Environment

d) Constraints

e) How would the product be manufactured commercially?

1. For the money box brief, talk to members of your family to find out what they would like the money box to do (for example, have flashing lights or play a musical tune to reward people every time they insert a coin); what shape, size and colour they would like the box to be, etc.

2. Analyse the project by answering the following questions:
   (The idea of this exercise is to start you thinking about all the options available to you.)

CASE

a) What would you make the case out of?

b) What size would it be?

c) What shape would it be?

d) How would it be held together?

e) How would it be finished?

f) How would the electronic circuitry and the batteries fit in?

g) How would you make it so the batteries can be easily accessed?

ELECTRONIC CIRCUITRY

h) Identify the input, process and output devices.

i) What calculations would you need to do?

j) What power supply would you need?

k) What would you use to design and test your circuit before you started to make the circuit board?

l) How could you find out how much the components cost?

1. For the money box project, write down FIVE questions that you could put on a questionnaire to seek people's opinions.

   i) ....

   ii) ....

   iii) ....

   iv) ....

   v) ....

2. Below are two tables that contain data that has been gathered from another questionnaire.

   How often do you play the lottery?

M/F	ONCE A WEEK OR MORE	ONCE A MONTH OR MORE	ONCE A YEAR OR MORE	NEVER
Male	19	8	4	9
Female	8	4	6	2

   Would you buy a device that selected numbers for you?

M/F	YES	NO
Male	10	30
Female	5	15

   a) How many people took part in the questionnaire? ....

   b) What percentage of respondents were female? ....

   c) What percentage of male respondents said they would purchase a device that selected numbers for them?

   ....

   d) Draw charts in the space provided below to display the information in the tables in a more meaningful way.

1. Observe an electronic product working and create a basic block system diagram for the process section.

INPUT	PROCESS	OUTPUT

2. Research different ways of making the various parts of the circuit. For each process part below, list THREE components that you could use to make it. Use the Rapid catalogue or website to help you.

a) For the input device:

i) ....
ii) ....
iii) ....

b) For one of the process devices:

i) ....
ii) ....
iii) ....

c) For the output device:

i) ....
ii) ....
iii) ....

3. Choose ONE component for each device above and give a reason why you chose it.

a) Input device ....
b) Process device ....
c) Output device ....

4. Write down THREE areas you could research further for this product.

i) ....
ii) ....
iii) ....

1. Why is it important to write a specification at the start of the project?

2. Create a specification for a commercially manufactured electronic product or one of the projects on page 6. Refer to page 22 of the Revision Guide and try to tackle each criterion.

3. Write ONE test that you could carry out on the product as part of the evaluation.

1. Look at an existing product or select one of the briefs from page 6. In the space below draw THREE different ideas for a case for this product that could be made out of suitable resistant materials. (See page 9 of the Revision Guide for hints of what you should include in your drawings.) Alternatively, you can use a CAD system to speed up the design process. If you use this method, don't forget to print off your design and stick it in the space below. Make sure you label construction methods, materials to be used, fixing devices, dimensions and show as much detail as possible with reference to colour and surface finish.

1. Name TWO ways you can test the design of your PCB.

   i) ....

   ii) ....

2. What is the distance between the pin connections on an IC? (Don't forget to include the unit!)

   ....

3. Which of these drawings have pin 1 labelled correctly?

   i)   ii)   iii)   iv)

   ....

4. Should you draw tracks so they go directly between the components they are to connect, or should you draw tracks so that they only go horizontally and vertically?

   ....

5. What can happen if you make the pads too small?

   ....

6. What can happen if you make the tracks too narrow?

   ....

7. What is the name of the etching solution used in the etching tank?

   ....

8. What is creating your PCB mask on a computer an example of?

   ....

1. The answers to the clues in this crossword relate to the process of making a PCB by the photographic method.

ACROSS

3, 5 and 7 across
What does PCB stand for? (7, 7, 5)

4 What is the name given to the process of transferring the mask onto the board to create the PCB? (7)

5 See 3 across

7 See 3 across

8 What is the name of the sheet that the artwork is copied on to? (7)

9 After the board has been in the light box, it is submersed in a mixture of liquids to .... (7)

DOWN

1 What is the name given to the regulations that you must adhere to when making products? (6, 3, 6)

2 What kind of light is used in the light box? (11)

5 What metal are the tracks made out of? (6)

6 What is the name given to the board that the mask of the PCB is transferred onto? (11)

---

2. Which one of the following is an example of quality assurance? (Tick the correct box)

i) Replacing the battery when it stops working ☐
ii) including strain holes for leads ☐
iii) painting it red because it's your favourite colour ☐

---

3. Which components should you put on the PCB last?

---

4. What polarity does red sleeving indicate?

---

5. What should you apply the tip of the soldering iron to when soldering? (Tick the correct box)

i) The lead that is to be soldered ☐
ii) The solder ☐
iii) The copper pad and the lead that is to be soldered ☐

1. The following are stages for constructing a case from timber. Put them in the correct order.

a) Rub down with fine glass paper
b) Cut and shape the parts
c) Design the case
d) Sand the parts
e) Varnish
f) Mark out all the required parts
g) Carry out final inspection
h) Check all the parts fit together
i) Join the parts together
j) Drill the parts

☐   ☐   ☐   ☐   ☐   ☐   ☐   ☐   ☐   ☐

2. Look around your home and identify a number of electronic products. Name the material the case is manufactured from and list the production methods used.

ELECTRONIC PRODUCT	MATERIAL	PRODUCTION METHOD

1. Look at the Rapid catalogue or website to make a list of all the components you would need in order to make the circuit shown below. Create your own table, but make sure you include the name of the item, the order code, the cost per item, the quantity required and the total cost. You could use ICT to produce your components list then print it off and stick it in the space below.

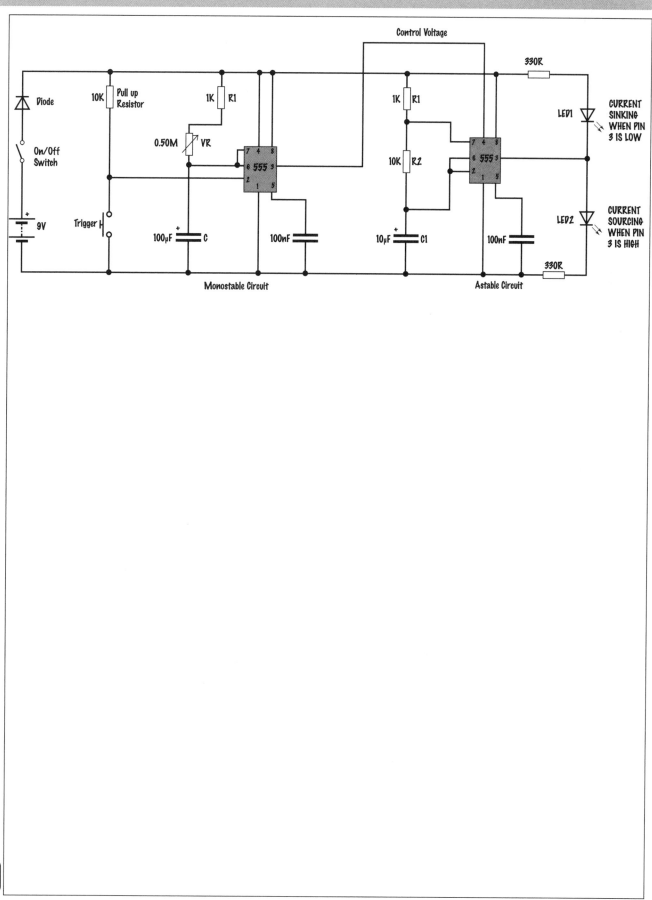

1. Why is it important to carry out testing throughout the design and making process?

2. List THREE tests you could carry out to find out if the product is suitable for the purpose it was designed for.

   i)

   ii)

   iii)

3. Where should you try to carry out these tests?

4. Other people's opinions are a useful starting point for a final evaluation report. List SIX questions you could ask.

   i)

   ii)

   iii)

   iv)

   v)

   vi)

5. Why is it important to check your prototype against your original specification?

6. What should you do if the prototype does not satisfy the specification?

7. Write down THREE questions that you should ask yourself when considering what modifications you need to make to your product.

   i)

   ii)

   iii)

8. Name THREE manufacturing aids that you could use if you had to produce 30 identical electronic products.

   i)   ii)   iii)

1. In the space below, draw a square, a circle and an equilateral triangle in freehand. Use a ballpoint pen or fineliner pen to force you to work accurately.

2. Based on the geometric shapes above, draw freehand front views of a watch and a lamp.

Watch design

Lamp design for a child's bedroom

3. Use the 'crating out' method to produce a 3D view of this toy train.

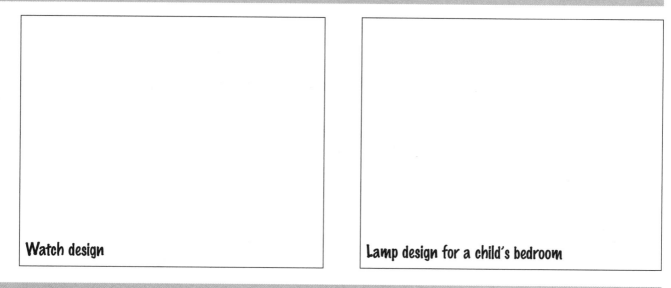

1. Using isometric projection, draw a cube which has sides of 50mm.

2. Re-draw the shed in isometric, using different dimensions to make it fill the space available.

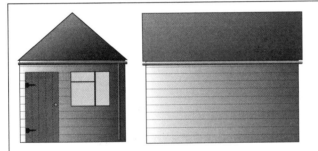

1. To demonstrate your ability to draw circles in isometric, produce a case design for an electronic die which has seven LEDs and two round rocker switches.

2. Refer back to your 3D drawing of the toy train (on page 17) and produce an exploded drawing to show how the wheels are attached to the base.

1. What THREE things should a working drawing show?

i) ....
ii) ....
iii) ....

2. The British Standards Institute has set standards for working drawings. Explain what the following lines are used for.

a) Continuous thick lines ....
b) Continuous thin lines ....
c) Chain thin lines ....

3. The British Standards Institute has also set standards for dimensioning working drawings.

a) What unit of measurement is used? ....
b) Why is this unit of measurement used? ....
c) Where are the dimensions written? ....

4. Dimension the drawing below to BSI standards.

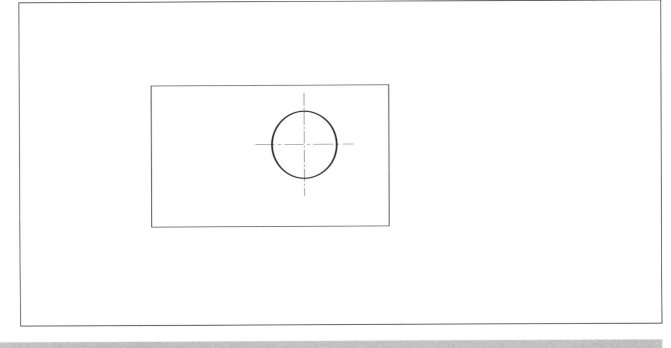

5. Explain what the drawing below indicates.

....
....
....
....

Revision Guide Reference: Page 39

1. What views does a third-angle orthographic projection give you?

2. Draw a third-angle orthographic projection of a mobile phone. Include the main dimensions and show the scale.

COMPUTER-AIDED MANUFACTURE, SCALES OF PRODUCTION & QUALITY ASSURANCE SYSTEMS

1. What is the difference between CAD and CAM?

2. Give ONE benefit of using CAD/CAM.

3. Give ONE advantage of producing a prototype before going straight into full-scale production.

4. Complete the table below.

NAME OF PRODUCTION	DESCRIPTION	EXAMPLE
	Product goes through various stages on a production line and workers are responsible for a certain part of a product. Product is produced for days or even weeks, and in large numbers.	
Just In Time		
		A display for an exhibition stand
	A series of products which are all the same are made together in either small or large quantities.	

5. Write down FOUR quality control tests that could be carried out on a product.

i)

ii)

iii)

iv)

6. Explain the term 'working to tolerance'

1. Commercial manufacturing consists of a system or group of sub-systems. Name FOUR requirements.

i) .... ii) ....

iii) .... iv) ....

2. Suggest THREE health and safety checks you would make before using a drilling machine

i) ....

ii) ....

iii) ....

3. Name THREE pieces of equipment you can wear to protect yourself when working in a workshop.

i) .... ii) .... iii) ....

4. Find a fire extinguisher in your workshop.

a) What does it contain? ....

b) What colour is it? ....

c) On what materials can it be used? ....

5. What should you do if you notice a fire?

i) ....

ii) ....

iii) ....

6. a) What do these symbols mean?

i) .... ii) ....

b) How can manufacturers get them on their products?

....

7. Write down an alternative to recycling and explain why this would reduce the damage inflicted on the environment.

1. As well as the properties of a material, what THREE other factors should you consider when choosing a material?

i) .... ii) .... iii) ....

2. What are the THREE plastics you should know about for your exam?

i) .... ii) .... iii) ....

3. Write down SIX properties of plastics.

i) .... ii) .... iii) ....
iv) .... v) .... vi) ....

4. What are the THREE timbers you should know about for your exam?

i) .... ii) .... iii) ....

5. Explain the following characteristics of timber:

a) workability ....
b) texture ....
c) grain pattern ....
d) structural strength ....
e) colour ....

6. What are the THREE metals you should know about for your exam?

i) .... ii) .... iii) ....

7. Draw lines to match each property to the correct explanation.

Toughness	The ability to be stretched without breaking
Ductility	How likely it is to break without bending
Work hardness	Ability to retain strength when under pressure
Compressive strength	Resistance to breaking, bending and deforming
Brittleness	Resistance to scratching, cutting and wear
Malleability	Ability to retain strength when stretched
Elasticity	The ability to regain its original shape after it has been deformed
Tensile strength	The ability to be easily pressed, spread or hammered into shape
Hardness	Ability of the structure of the metal to change after hammering or strain

1. a) Name the TWO types of plastic.

i) .... ii) ....

b) Explain, using diagrams and notes, the differences between the two types of plastic.
Refer to: i) the structure, ii) the effect of heat, iii) the environment.

2. Insert the names of the THREE plastics you should know about for your course. Then match the properties to the varieties of plastic.

Stiff and very brittle when cold

Highly resistant to impact

Thermoplastic material

Can be processed industrially by injection moulding, blow moulding or vacuum forming

Ten times more resistant to impact than glass

Easy to cut and drill

Available in transparent, coloured translucent or coloured opaque sheets

Available in many forms including sheets, blocks, rods and tubes

Quite flexible in sheet form

3. For each item, choose a suitable plastic and explain the reason for your choice.

a) Car bumper
Plastic ....
Reason ....

b) Food container
Plastic ....
Reason ....

c) The case for your electronic product
Plastic ....
Reason ....

1. a) Sort the properties below into the correct columns in the table provided:

Comes from coniferous trees

Comes from slow-growing trees

Made by gluing together wood layers or fibres

Softer and easier to work than other types

Can be made in a consistent quality

Comes from broad-leafed or deciduous trees

HARDWOOD	SOFTWOOD	MANUFACTURED BOARD

b) In the bottom row of the table above, write an example of each type of timber.

2. Complete the following statements by crossing out the incorrect answer:

a) CHIPBOARD / PLYWOOD is constructed from an odd number of thin layers of wood glued together.

b) PLYWOOD / MDF is available with a veneered finish.

c) PINE / BALSA is a hardwood.

d) MDF / PLYWOOD has a uniform strength throughout.

e) PINE AND MDF / PINE AND PLYWOOD / MDF AND PLYWOOD have a grain.

f) MDF / PINE is useful for creating moulds for vacuum forming due to its closely structured core.

3. Give ONE use for each type of timber:

a) Pine ....

b) Plywood ....

c) MDF ....

4. Name SIX types of manufactured board.

i) .... ii) .... iii) ....

iv) .... v) .... vi) ....

5. In the space below, draw a sketch of a cross-section of plywood and explain why it is made in this way.

1. Sort the properties below into the correct columns in the table provided.

| Brass is a typical example | Are attracted to a magnet | Consist mainly of iron |
| Copper and aluminium are typical examples | Contain no iron at all | Contain two or more metals |

ALLOYS	FERROUS METALS	NON-FERROUS METALS

2. The answers to the clues in this crossword relate to metals and their properties.

ACROSS

4 Small containers that are made from 6 down (5, 4)

7 A method of fusing two or more sections of steel together (7)

8 see 1 down

9 One reason for mixing metals is to reduce the .... point (7)

10 Mild steel is available in many forms including sheeting, strips, bars and ...... (6)

11 The results of mixing two or more metals together (6)

DOWN

1 and 8 across A large object that you can find in your house that is made out of copper (3, 5, 8)

2 One method of machining steel (7)

3 A metal that is often mixed with aluminium (3)

5 Most common type of steel in use (4, 5)

6 Most common metal found on earth (9)

1. Name the following tools.

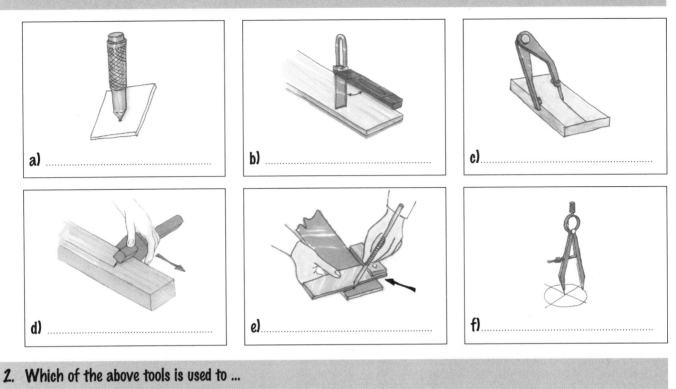

a) ....

b) ....

c) ....

d) ....

e) ....

f) ....

2. Which of the above tools is used to ...

a) scribe lines parallel to a straight edge of timber? ....

b) mark the centre of a hole when drilling into metal? ....

c) mark out circles or arcs? ....

d) mark out lines at any angle? ....

3. Card templates are often used for marking out curved surfaces on to any material. Explain, using diagrams, how you would use a card template to mark out a symmetrical Teddy Bear shape.

4. Show how you would mark out two 6mm diameter holes, centrally and 10mm from each end of the material below.

1. Name the following holding devices.

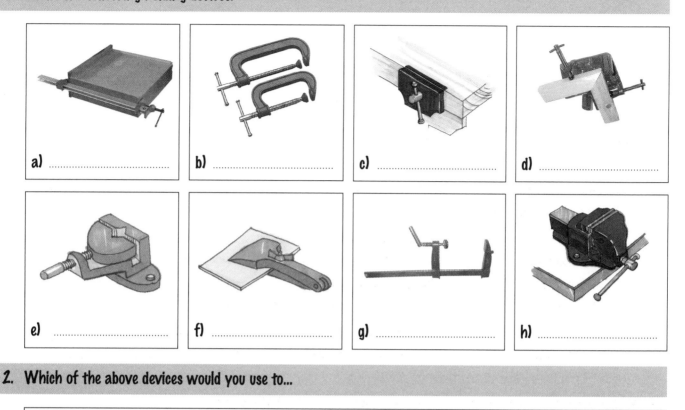

a) ....

b) ....

c) ....

d) ....

e) ....

f) ....

g) ....

h) ....

2. Which of the above devices would you use to...

a) hold wooden joints together whilst gluing? ....

b) hold timber and plastics to the workbench? ....

c) hold a material which is being drilled? ....

d) hold materials at right angles to join them together? ....

3. What is a toggle clamp used for?

....

4. Suggest two benefits of using a jig when producing large quantities of a product.

i) ....   ii) ....

5. Fixtures are production aids which are attached to machines. Design a fixture which will allow 5mm holes for LEDs to be drilled every 30mm in the centre of a strip of 20mm wide perspex.

1. How many teeth on a saw should be in contact with the material at any one time?

2. Name a saw which has a blade held in tension within a frame.

3. Name a saw which has the blade fixed directly to the handle.

4. Below are the names of FIVE power saws and simple descriptions of how they work. Match each power saw to the correct description.

Powered hacksaw	Saw blade is rotated as material is moved across the blade.
Scroll saw	Blade has a forward/backward motion which copies the manual version.
Circular saw	A continuous strip of saw blade is rotated.
Jigsaw	Blade is held in tension and has a reciprocating action.
Bandsaw	Blade is pushed through the material using a reciprocating motion.

5. Explain how you would cut the shape below from 5mm thick MDF sheet.

6. Name the following chisels.

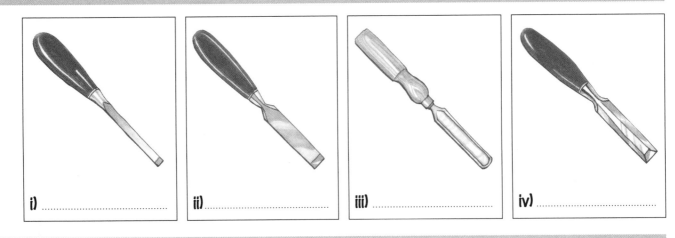

i) .... ii) .... iii) .... iv) ....

7. Name the THREE basic chiselling actions.

i) ....

ii) ....

iii) ....

1. Name the following planes.

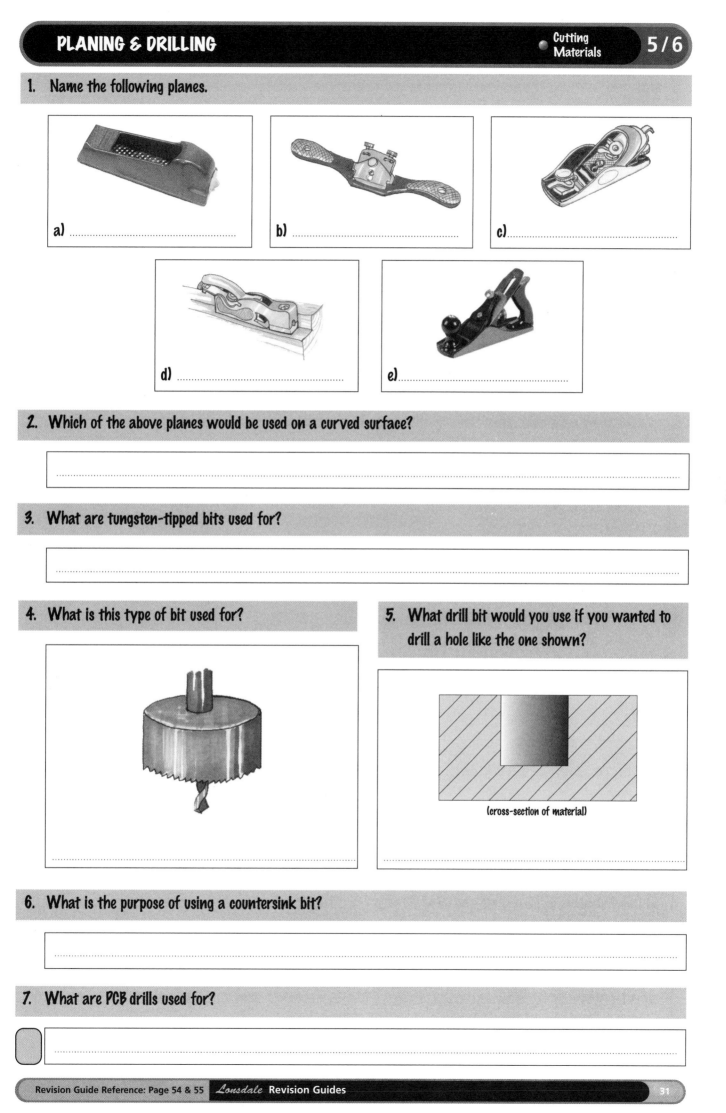

a) ....

b) ....

c) ....

d) ....

e) ....

2. Which of the above planes would be used on a curved surface?

....

3. What are tungsten-tipped bits used for?

....

4. What is this type of bit used for?

....

5. What drill bit would you use if you wanted to drill a hole like the one shown?

(cross-section of material)

....

6. What is the purpose of using a countersink bit?

....

7. What are PCB drills used for?

....

1. a) In what way are the processes of milling and routing the same?

....

b) In what way are milling and routing different?

....

2. a) Name the process being shown in the diagram.   ....

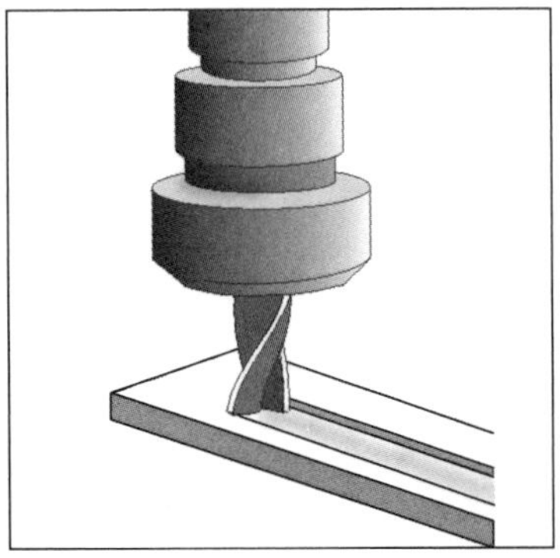

b) On the diagram, show the direction the cutter is rotating.

c) On the diagram, show the direction the table is moving in.

3. Explain, using a diagram, what the x, y, and z axis do in a milling machine.

4. Explain, very simply, the process involved in CNC milling.

....

5. a) Explain the process involved in turning.

....

b) How does a centre lathe work?

....

c) In what ways is a wood-turning lathe different to a centre lathe?

....

d) What would be the main advantage of using a CNC lathe (rather than a manual lathe)?

....

1. Name FOUR abrasive materials which are glued onto a paper or cloth backing.

i) .... ii) ....

iii) .... iv) ....

2. Each sheet of abrasive paper/cloth has a number printed on the back. What does the number signify?

....

3. What is the function of water when used with 'wet and dry' paper?

....

4. Why is a cork block used with abrasive paper?

....

5. Draw and label the cross-sections of FIVE common files.

i)	ii)	iii)	iv)	v)

6. State ONE difference between using a belt sander and a disk sander.

....

....

7. Hand-held power sanders create additional safety hazards. Name TWO and explain what can be done to reduce the risk to the health and safety of fellow pupils.

i) Hazard ....

   Reduce the risk by... ....

ii) Hazard ....

   Reduce the risk by... ....

1. Name the following joints.

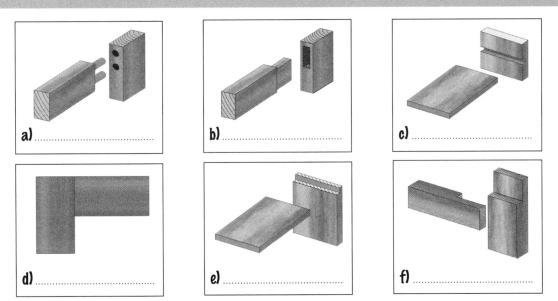

a) ....

b) ....

c) ....

d) ....

e) ....

f) ....

2. a) Nails can be used to secure joints. Give ONE disadvantage of using nails.

b) How can this be overcome?

3. What are the benefits of mechanical joining over thermal joining?

4. What is the difference between a bolt and a machine screw?

5. Draw FOUR different bolt heads in the boxes below.

6. Give ONE advantage and ONE disadvantage of using a rivet to join materials together compared with using a nut and bolt.

Advantage ....

Disadvantage ....

1. Explain, using a labelled diagram, how an internal thread can be cut by hand.

2. Explain, using a labelled diagram, how an external thread can be cut by hand.

3. For each pair of materials: i) state which adhesive you would use to stick them together, and ii) explain how that adhesive works.

a) Plastic and plastic.

i) ....

ii) ....

b) Metal and metal.

i) ....

ii) ....

c) Metal and wood.

i) ....

ii) ....

d) Wood and wood.

i) ....

ii) ....

e) Plastic and wood.

i) ....

ii) ....

New College Nottingham

1. Complete the table.

TYPE OF PAINT	PRODUCT IT MIGHT BE USED ON	CLEAN IT UP WITH

2. Name THREE types of finish that varnishes are available in.

i) .... ii) .... iii) ....

3. a) Why are wood stains used?

....

b) Why is wax or varnish needed on top of wood stain?

....

4. Explain the purpose of sanding sealer.

....
....

5. Explain the THREE stages used in the process of dip-coating.

i) ....
ii) ....
iii) ....

6. What is the name given to the industrial process that is a more sophisticated version of dip-coating?

....

7. a) What does the term self-finishing mean?

....

b) Give an example of a form of manufacturing that produces a self-finished product.

....

1. Name FOUR materials that can be injection moulded.

i) .... ii) ....

iii) .... iv) ....

b) Briefly explain the process of injection moulding.

....

....

....

....

....

2. a) Name THREE materials that can be blow moulded.

i) ....

ii) ....

iii) ....

b) Explain the process of blow moulding, using diagrams to help you.

....

....

....

....

3. a) What is the most popular material to be vacuum formed?

....

b) Why is the plastic heated up?

....

c) Why is the air sucked out?

....

4. a) What type of plastic can be shaped by line bending?

....

b) What could you use to help you if you wanted to create 50 identical items?

....

1. Why should you not use mains electricity as the energy source for your project?

....
....
....

2. What type of energy does a battery contain?

....

3. Give TWO requirements you need to consider when selecting a battery for your project.

i) ....
ii) ....

4. Label the batteries in the space provided. The first one has been done for you.

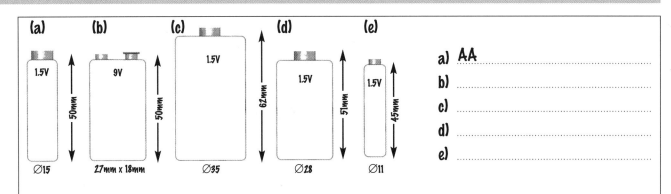

a) AA ....
b) ....
c) ....
d) ....
e) ....

5. Give ONE advantage and ONE disadvantage of using the following batteries:

BATTERY	ADVANTAGE	DISADVANTAGE
Zinc Carbon		
Alkaline		
Silver Oxide		
Lithium (non-rechargeable)		
Nickel Cadmium (rechargeable)		

1. Draw the circuit symbol for the following switches.

a) Single pole double throw	b) Double pole double throw	c) Single pole single throw

2. What is the difference between a single pole single throw switch and a single pole double throw switch?

....

3. Give TWO uses for a double pole double throw switch.

i) ....

ii) ....

4. Name the following mechanical switches.

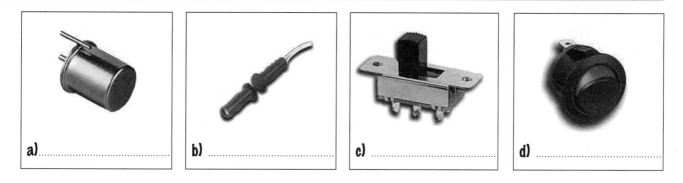

a) ....   b) ....   c) ....   d) ....

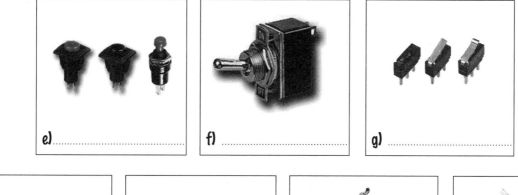

e) ....   f) ....   g) ....

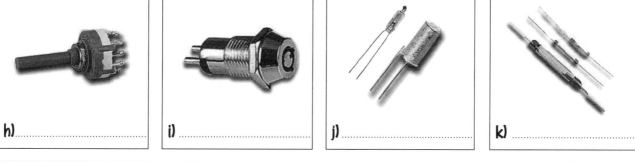

h) ....   i) ....   j) ....   k) ....

1. Give TWO uses for a resistor in an electronic circuit.

    i) ....

    ii) ....

2. Rewrite the following resistances using the multipliers R, K and M.

    i) 150 Ohms ....   ii) 1 800 Ohms ....

    iii) 3.3 Ohms ....   iv) 12 000 000 Ohms ....

    v) 5 600 Ohms ....   vi) 10 Ohms ....

    vii) 82 000 000 Ohms ....   viii) 47 Ohms ....

    ix) 3 300 Ohms ....   x) 7.5 Ohms ....

3. Complete the following table by working out the value and tolerance of the following resistors. You are given the four colours of the bands on the resistors.

BAND 1	BAND 2	BAND 3	BAND 4	RESISTOR VALUE AND TOLERANCE
brown	green	red	gold	
red	red	yellow	silver	
yellow	violet	black	silver	
green	blue	blue	gold	
violet	green	orange	gold	

4. Complete the following table by working out the colours of the four bands of the following resistors. You are given the value and tolerance of each resistor

RESISTOR VALUE AND TOLERANCE	BAND 1	BAND 2	BAND 3	BAND 4
560R ±5%				
68K ±10%				
1M8 ±10%				
8K2 ±5%				
22M ±5%				

5. Complete the following table by selecting resistors from the E12 and E24 series.

RESISTOR VALUE AND TOLERANCE	BAND 1	BAND 2	BAND 3	BAND 4
.... ±10%	green	....	brown	....
.... ±10%	....	red	yellow	....
.... ±5%	violet	....	red	....
....	blue	....	red	silver
....	....	brown	orange	gold

6. Why are resistors produced with a certain number of preferred values to a particular tolerance?

7. Give TWO differences between the resistors from the E12 series and those from the E24 series.

i) ....

ii) ....

8. Use arrows to match the THREE types of resistor to their circuit symbol and what they look like.

COMPONENT	CIRCUIT SYMBOL	WHAT IT LOOKS LIKE
Preset potentiometer or variable resistor		
Rotary potentiometer or variable resistor		
Slide potentiometer or variable resistor		

9. a) What is the purpose of using a current limiting resistor in a circuit?

b) Name TWO components that are protected by using a current limiting resistor.

i) ....   ii) ....

1. Put a tick (✔) in each box that represents the correct formula for the relationship between current, voltage and resistance.

voltage = $\dfrac{current}{resistance}$ ☐	voltage = $\dfrac{resistance}{current}$ ☐	voltage = current x resistance ☐
current = $\dfrac{voltage}{resistance}$ ☐	current = $\dfrac{resistance}{voltage}$ ☐	current = voltage x resistance ☐
resistance = $\dfrac{current}{voltage}$ ☐	resistance = $\dfrac{voltage}{current}$ ☐	resistance = current x voltage ☐

2. **a)** What current passes through a 12R resistor if the voltage across it is 6 volts?

Formula: ....
....
Working: ....
....
Answer with units: ....

b) What current passes through a 2K resistor if the voltage across it is 9 volts?

Formula: ....
....
Working: ....
....
Answer with units: ....

c) A current of 4mA passes through a 2K resistor. What is the voltage across the resistor?

Formula: ....
....
Working: ....
....
Answer with units: ....

d) A current of 2μA passes through a 1M resistor. What is the voltage across the resistor?

Formula: ....
....
Working: ....
....
Answer with units: ....

e) Calculate the resistance of a resistor if a current of 3mA passes through it when the voltage across it is 9 volts.

Formula: ....
....
Working: ....
....
Answer with units: ....

f) Calculate the resistance of a resistor if a current of 1.8μA passes through it when the voltage across it is 9 volts.

Formula: ....
....
Working: ....
....
Answer with units: ....

1. Calculate the total resistance of the following resistors connected in series.

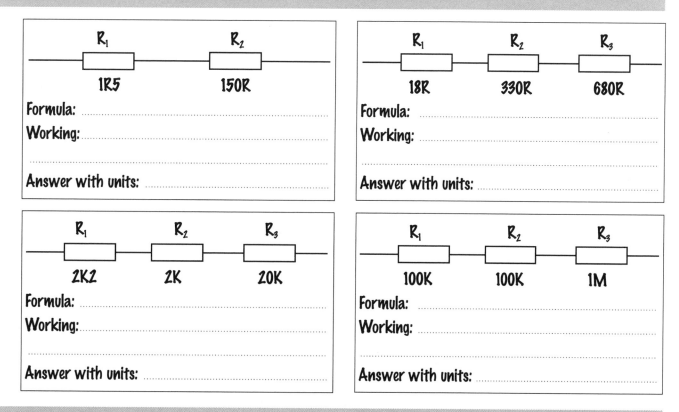

R₁ 1R5 R₂ 150R	R₁ 18R R₂ 330R R₃ 680R
Formula:	Formula: ....
Working:	Working: ....
....	....
Answer with units:	Answer with units: ....
R₁ 2K2 R₂ 2K R₃ 20K	R₁ 100K R₂ 100K R₃ 1M
Formula:	Formula: ....
Working:	Working: ....
....	....
Answer with units:	Answer with units: ....

2. When two or more resistors are connected in series, the same amount of electrical current passes through each resistor. In the following combination, a current of 1.5mA passes through each resistor.

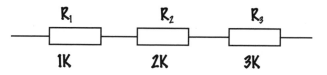

R₁ 1K   R₂ 2K   R₃ 3K

a) Calculate the voltage across:

i) resistor R1   ii) resistor R2   iii) resistor R3

Formula:	Formula:	Formula: ....
Working:	Working:	Working: ....
Answer with units:	Answer with units:	Answer with units: ....

b) What is the total voltage across the combination of resistors above?

....

c) If the total voltage across the combination of resistors above was 3 volts, what current would pass through each resistor?

Formula: ....
Working: ....
Answer with units: ....

1. Calculate the total resistance of the following resistors connected in parallel.

a)

R_1
10R
R_2
10R

Formula: ....

Working: ....
....
....
....
....
....
....
....
....

Answer with units: ....
....

b)

R_1
20R
R_2
30R

Formula: ....

Working: ....
....
....
....
....
....
....
....
....

Answer with units: ....
....

c)

R_1
10R
R_2
20R
R_3
30R

Formula: ....

Working: ....
....
....
....
....
....
....

Answer with units: ....
....

d)

R_1
1K
R_2
1K

Formula: ....

Working: ....
....
....
....
....
....
....
....
....

Answer with units: ....
....

2. When two or more resistors are connected in parallel, the voltage across each resistor is the same. In the following combination a voltage of 9 volts is across each resistor.

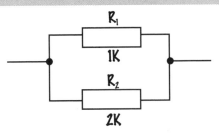

R_1
1K
R_2
2K

a) i) What current passes through resistor R_1?

Formula: ....

Working: ....
....
....

Answer with units: ....

ii) What current passes through resistor R_1?

Formula: ....

Working: ....
....
....

Answer with units: ....

b) What is the total current in the circuit above?

....

1. Calculate the voltage signal, Vs, for each of the following potential dividers. The supply voltage for each potential divider is 6 volts.

a)

+6V ○———————○ +6V

R_1 10K

———————○ Vs

R_2 10K

0V ○———————○ 0V

Formula: ....

Working: ....

....

....

....

....

....

....

....

....

....

Answer with units: ....

b)

+6V ○———————○ +6V

R_1 10K

———————○ Vs

R_2 20K

0V ○———————○ 0V

Formula: ....

Working: ....

....

....

....

....

....

....

....

....

....

Answer with units: ....

c)

+6V ○———————○ +6V

R_1 30K

———————○ Vs

R_2 10K

0V ○———————○ 0V

Formula: ....

Working: ....

....

....

....

....

....

....

....

....

....

Answer with units: ....

2. a) When the supply voltage, V, to a potential divider is 9 volts, the voltage signal, Vs, is 6 volts. Choose TWO suitable resistor values from the E24 series for R_1 and R_2 for the potential divider. Explain your choice.

b) Choose TWO suitable resistor values from the E24 series for R_1 and R_2 if the voltage signal, Vs, is a quarter of the supply voltage, V, in a potential divider. Explain your choice.

1. The graph shows how the amount of light falling on a light dependent resistor affects its resistance. Explain the shape of the graph and sketch what an LDR looks like.

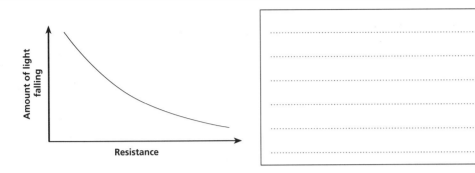

Resistance

Amount of light falling

....
....
....
....
....
....

Sketch of LDR

2. The diagram shows an LDR as part of a potential divider. Explain what happens to the voltage signal, Vs, when the light intensity on the LDR increases.

+V   +V
Vs
0V   0V

....
....
....
....
....
....

3. What is the difference between a negative coefficient thermistor and a positive temperature coefficient thermistor?

....
....

4. Draw a potential divider that includes a negative type thermistor and variable resistor where Vs changes from low to high when the temperature of the thermistor increases. Explain the positioning of the thermistor and variable resistor.

....
....
....
....
....
....

5. What is the advantage of including a variable resistor rather than a resistor of known resistance in a potential divider that includes either an LDR or a thermistor?

....
....

1. Put a tick (✔) in each box that represents the correct formula for the relationship between power, voltage and current.

power = $\dfrac{voltage}{current}$ ☐	power = $\dfrac{current}{voltage}$ ☐	power = voltage x current ☐
voltage = $\dfrac{power}{current}$ ☐	voltage = $\dfrac{current}{power}$ ☐	voltage = power x current ☐
current = $\dfrac{power}{voltage}$ ☐	current = $\dfrac{voltage}{power}$ ☐	current = power x voltage ☐

2. a) A resistor has a voltage of 6 volts across it. Calculate its resistance and choose a suitable resistor from the E12 or E24 series if the maximum current that passes through the resistor is 15mA.

Formula: ....
Working: ....
....
Answer with units: .... Chosen resistor ....

b) Calculate the power rating of the resistor.

Formula: ....
Working: ....
Answer with units: ....

3. A current limiting resistor in series with an LED is needed to allow a maximum current of 20mA to pass through the LED. The total voltage across the resistor and LED is 6 volts, of which 2 volts are across the LED.

a) Calculate the resistance of the current limiting resistor and choose a suitable resistor from the E12 or E24 series.

Formula: ....
Working: ....
Answer with units: .... Chosen resistor ....

b) Calculate the power rating of the current limiting resistor.

Formula: ....
Working: ....
Answer with units: ....

1. What do capacitors store in electronic circuits?

2. Give TWO uses for capacitors in electronic circuits.

   i) ....
   ii) ....

3. Give THREE units of capacitance (apart from the Farad) that most capacitors are measured in. For each unit, state how its value relates to the Farad.

   i) Unit: ....
   How value relates to the Farad: ....

   ii) Unit: ....
   How value relates to the Farad: ....

   iii) Unit: ....
   How value relates to the Farad: ....

4. Why is it important for all capacitors to display on their cases the maximum working voltage?

5. a) In the boxes provided below, draw the circuit symbol for an electrolytic capacitor and for a non-electrolytic capacitor.

Electrolytic	Non-electrolytic

   b) Give THREE differences between electrolytic capacitors and non-electrolytic capacitors.

   i) ....
   ....
   ii) ....
   ....
   iii) ....
   ....

1. a) What is a dielectric?

b) Why will there always be a leakage current with a capacitor?

2. Calculate the time constant of the following capacitor and resistor combinations.

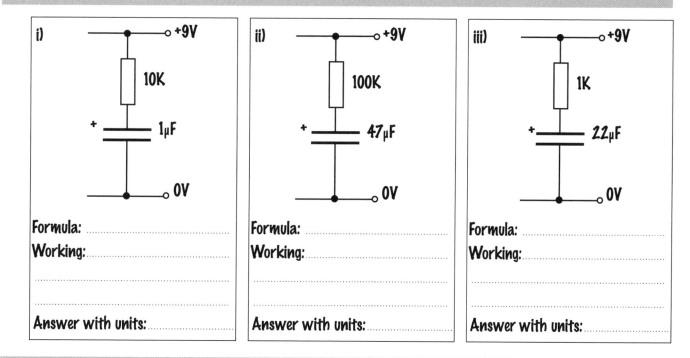

i)   +9V
10K
+   1μF
0V

Formula:
Working:

Answer with units:

ii)   +9V
100K
+   47μF
0V

Formula:
Working:

Answer with units:

iii)   +9V
1K
+   22μF
0V

Formula:
Working:

Answer with units:

3. The graph shows the voltage across a capacitor that is being charged through a resistor.

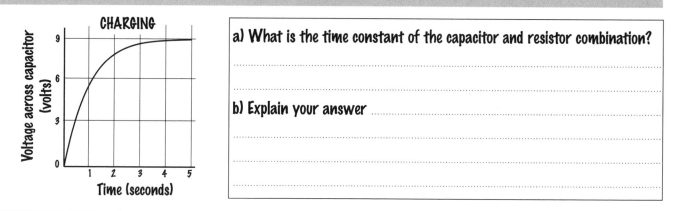

CHARGING

Voltage across capacitor (volts)

Time (seconds)

a) What is the time constant of the capacitor and resistor combination?

b) Explain your answer

4. Why are electrolytic capacitors only manufactured in multiples of 1, 2.2 and 4.7?

1. Calculate the total capacitance of the following combinations of capacitors.

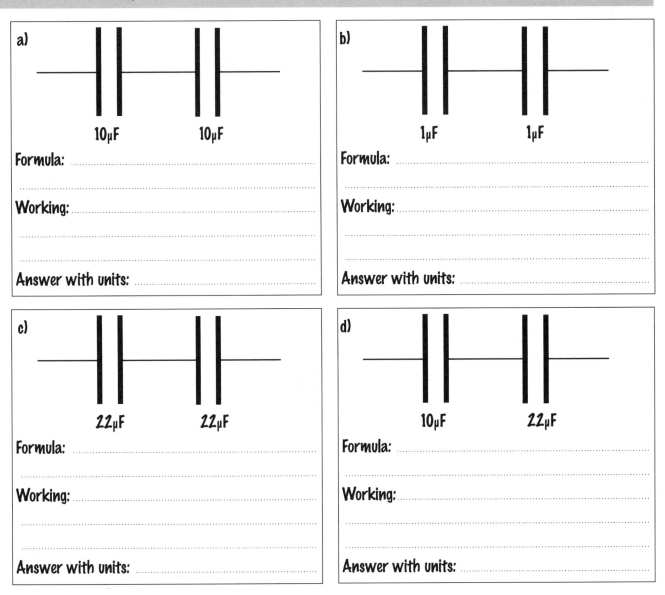

a)

10μF   10μF

Formula: ....

Working: ....

....

....

Answer with units: ....

b)

1μF   1μF

Formula: ....

Working: ....

....

....

Answer with units: ....

c)

22μF   22μF

Formula: ....

Working: ....

....

....

Answer with units: ....

d)

10μF   22μF

Formula: ....

Working: ....

....

....

Answer with units: ....

2. A student needs a capacitor with a value of 20μF. He decides to connect two 10μF capacitors in series. Without any calculations, explain why this combination is wrong.

....

....

....

5. Draw a radial and an axial electrolytic capacitor. Label the leads of the capacitors to show polarity.

Radial

Axial

4. Calculate the total capacitance of the following combinations of capacitors.

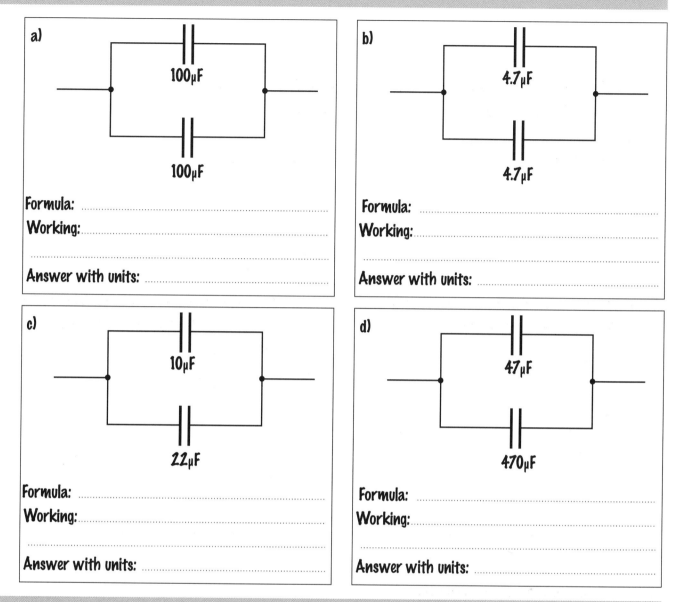

a)

100μF

100μF

Formula: ....

Working: ....

....

Answer with units: ....

b)

4.7μF

4.7μF

Formula: ....

Working: ....

....

Answer with units: ....

c)

10μF

22μF

Formula: ....

Working: ....

....

Answer with units: ....

d)

47μF

470μF

Formula: ....

Working: ....

....

Answer with units: ....

5. Calculate the total capacitance of the following combinations of capacitors.

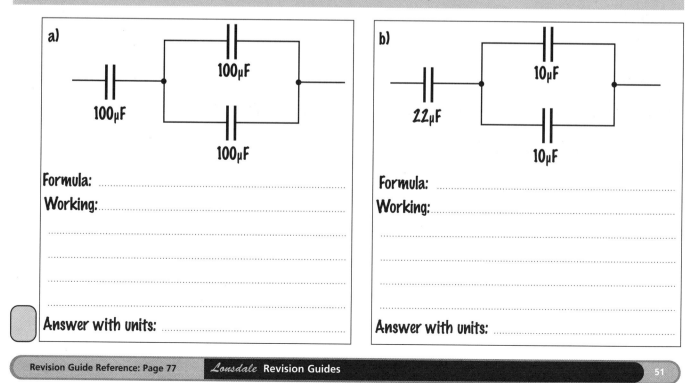

a)

100μF

100μF

100μF

Formula: ....

Working: ....

....

....

....

Answer with units: ....

b)

10μF

22μF

10μF

Formula: ....

Working: ....

....

....

....

Answer with units: ....

1.   a) What is a diode?

b) i) Draw the circuit symbol for a diode and label the anode and the cathode.

ii) Sketch what it looks like and label the anode and cathode.

Circuit symbol

Sketch of what it looks like

2.   a) Complete the following diagram by including a diode so that the lamp stays off when the switch is closed.

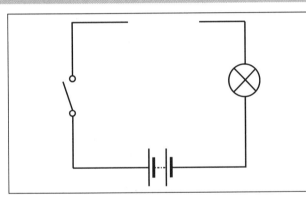

b)   Complete the following diagram by including a diode so that the lamp comes on when the switch is closed.

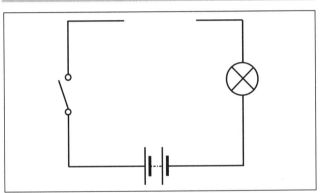

3.   Give THREE uses for diodes in circuits.

i)

ii)

iii)

4.   The diagram shows a diode in a circuit. Explain fully its purpose in this circuit.

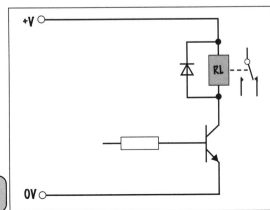

1. a) What is a light emitting diode?

    ....

    b) i) Draw the circuit symbol for a light emitting diode and label the anode and the cathode.
    ii) Sketch what it looks like and label the anode, cathode and flat.

Circuit symbol	Sketch of what it looks like

2. When using an LED in a circuit why should you always include a resistor in series with it?

    ....

3. a) i) A resistor is used in series with an LED. The LED needs a voltage of about 2 volts to make it work. The total voltage across the resistor and LED is 9 volts. Calculate the resistance of the resistor if a maximum current of 20mA is to pass through the LED.

    Formula: ....

    ....

    Working: ....

    ....

    ....

    ....

    Answer with units: ....

    ii) Choose a suitable resistor from the E12 series to use and explain your choice.

    Chosen resistor: ....

    ....

    ....

    ....

    ....

    ....

    b) i) A resistor is used in series with an LED. Again the LED needs a voltage of about 2 volts to make it work. The total voltage across the resistor and LED is 12 volts. Calculate the resistance of the resistor if a maximum current of 20mA is to pass through the LED.

    Formula: ....

    ....

    Working: ....

    ....

    ....

    ....

    Answer with units: ....

    ii) Choose a suitable resistor from the E24 series and explain your choice.

    Chosen resistor: ....

    ....

    ....

    ....

    ....

    ....

1. The diagram shows a 4017 IC decade counter with its outputs driving six output LEDs. The LEDs light up in the sequence: 1, 2, 3, 4, 5, 6, 5, 4, 3, 2, etc. The circuit includes eight steering diodes in order for the LEDs to light in this sequence.

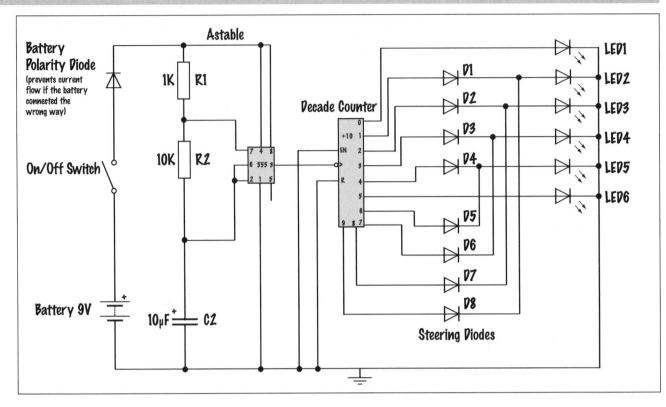

Complete the following table to show what happens in order to get the above sequence of LEDs. The first two have been done for you.

DECADE COUNTER PIN	LED THAT LIGHTS UP	DIODE THAT IS FORWARD BIASED	DIODE THAT IS REVERSE BIASED
0	LED 1	NONE	NONE
1	LED 2	D1	D8
2			
3			
4			
5			
6			
7			
8			
9			

1. A 7-segment LED display can be used to show numbers from 0 to 9. Each segment location is given a specific letter (a to g) as shown in the diagram.

Complete the following table by ticking which segments need to be lit in order to produce each number. The first one has been done for you.

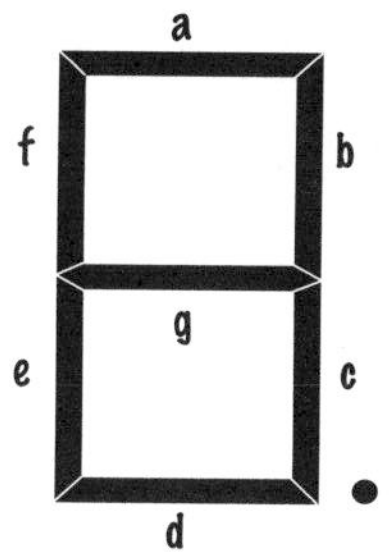

NUMBER PRODUCED	SEGMENT LIT						
	a	b	c	d	e	f	g
0	✓	✓	✓	✓	✓	✓	
1							
2							
3							
4							
5							
6							
7							
8							
9							

2. Give TWO differences between a common cathode 7-segment LED display and a common anode 7-segment LED display.

i) ....

....

ii) ....

....

3. Explain with the aid of a diagram how you would attach flying leads to an LED.

1. In the spaces below draw the circuit symbols for an npn transistor and a pnp transistor. For each symbol label the leads.

npn transistor	pnp transistor

2. What is the difference between an npn transistor and a pnp transistor?

....
....

3. Are the following statements about bipolar transistors TRUE or FALSE?

a) The leads of a transistor are called the base, collector and emitter.

....

b) A bipolar transistor is controlled by applying a voltage of more than 0.7 volts to its collector.

....

c) There is a high resistance between the collector and emitter when a transistor is switched off.

....

d) A transistor is an analogue device.

....

e) A transistor allows a large current to flow from the collector to the emitter as the base current decreases.

....

f) A transistor is fully switched on if there is a voltage of about 1.5volts between the base and emitter.

....

g) Transistors are used as current amplifiers.

....

h) Transistors are electronic switches.

....

i) Transistors are made from semi-conductor material.

....

1. What does 'gain' mean when it is used in connection with transistors?

2. a) Calculate the gain of a BC548 transistor if the collector current is 80mA when the base current is 0.4mA.

Formula:

Working:

Answer:

b) Calculate the gain of a BC639 transistor if the collector current is 120mA and the base current is 3mA.

Formula:

Working:

Answer:

3. a) The ^{h}FE gain of a BC548 is 225 when the collector current is 90mA. Calculate the base current.

Formula:

Working:

Answer with units:

b) Calculate the emitter current if the collector current is 100mA and base current is 0.5mA.

Formula:

Working:

Answer with units:

4. When the base current of a BC639 transistor is 3.5mA its ^{h}FE gain is 40. Calculate the collector current.

Formula:

Working:

Answer with units:

5. Draw THREE different types of transistor case styles and label the base, collector and emitter.

1. The circuit shows a BC548 transistor being used to switch on an output LED.

a) What is the purpose of the diode in series with the 9 volt power supply?

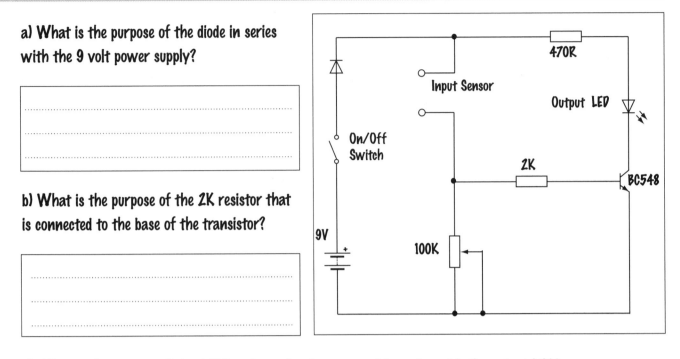

b) What is the purpose of the 2K resistor that is connected to the base of the transistor?

c) What is the purpose of the 470R resistor that is connected in series with the output LED?

d) Explain why the LED lights up when the resistance of the input sensor decreases sufficiently.

2. The circuit shows a Darlington driver being used to switch on a buzzer.

a) Explain very simply how the circuit works.

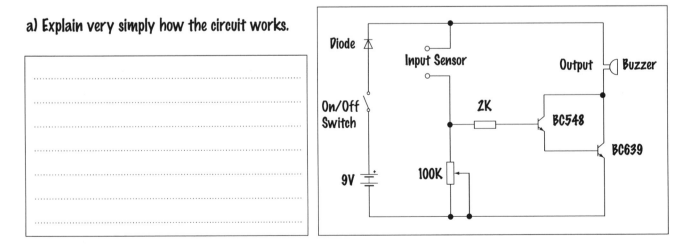

b) If the gain of a BC548 transistor is 220 and the gain of a BC639 transistor is 40, calculate the gain of the Darlington driver.

1. a) Draw the symbol for a field effect transistor (FET).

Circuit symbol (label e ach lead)

b) Sketch what a FET looks like.

Sketch of what it looks like

2. How does a FET work?

....

....

3. Why is a FET an example of a digital switching device?

....

....

4. Why are logic ICs and PICs often interfaced with FETs in electronic circuits?

....

....

5. The circuit shows a FET being used to switch on a motor.

a) Explain why the motor is switched on when the touch contacts are bridged with a finger.

....

....

....

....

....

....

....

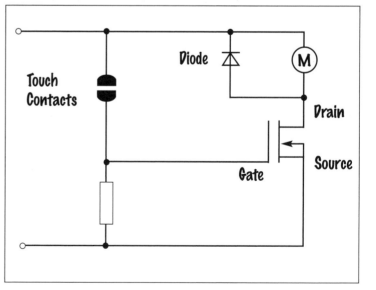

Touch Contacts

Diode (M)

Drain

Source

Gate

b) What is the purpose of the reverse-biased diode across the motor?

....

....

1. a) Draw the circuit symbol for a thyristor

b) Sketch what a thyristor looks like.

Circuit symbol (label each lead)

Sketch of what it looks like

2. a) A thyristor is an example of a bistable electronic device. Explain what that means.

b) When does a thyristor allow a current to flow from its anode to its cathode?

c) A thyristor is an example of an electronic latch. Explain what that means.

d) Explain how a thyristor is reset once it has been switched on.

3. a) The diagram shows the back view of a 106D thyristor. Label each lead.

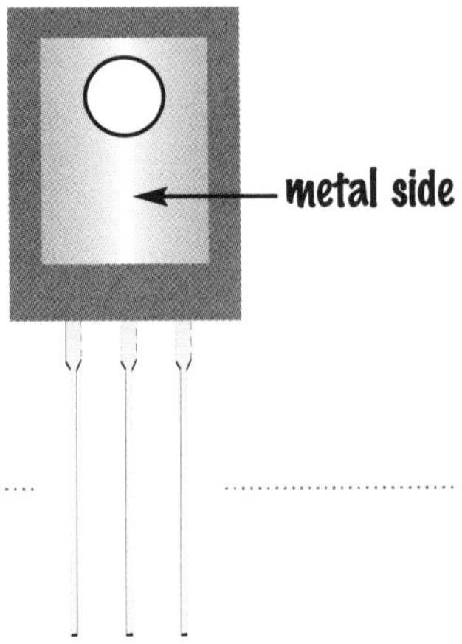

← metal side

b) Explain very simply how you would colour code a thyristor.

1. The circuit shows a thyristor being used to switch a buzzer on and off.

a) Explain why the buzzer is switched on when the set switch is pressed.

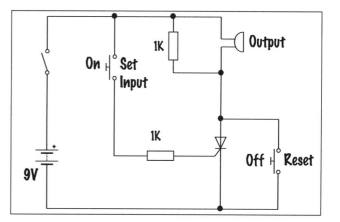

b) Explain why the buzzer is switched off when the reset switch is pressed.

c) What is the purpose of the 1K resistor in parallel with the buzzer?

2. a) Complete the diagram with a 100K resistor and touch contacts so that the buzzer is switched on when the touch contacts are bridged with a finger.

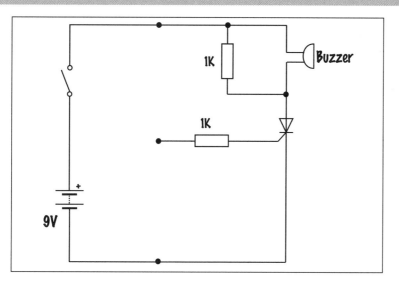

b) Explain why the buzzer is switched on when the touch contacts are bridged with a finger.

1. a) What is a piezo electric transducer?

b) In the space below draw the circuit symbol for a piezo electric transducer.

c) Why is a piezo electric transducer a very good sensor in many applications?

d) What is the purpose of the 1K resistor connected to the gate of the thyristor shown in the circuit below?

2. The circuit shows a piezo input being used to switch on a buzzer.

a) Explain how the circuit works.

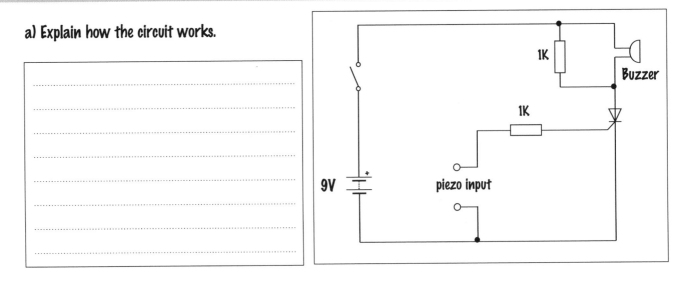

b) Explain how the buzzer is switched off.

1. a) What are relays used for?

b) What are the disadvantages of using a relay in a circuit?

2. a) The diagram shows a relay. Label it using the following.

PIVOT	COIL	COIL CONNECTION	CONNECTIONS TO EXTERNAL CIRCUIT
SPRINGY METAL	SWITCH CONTACTS	SOFT IRON CORE	
INSULATION			SOFT IRON ARMATURE

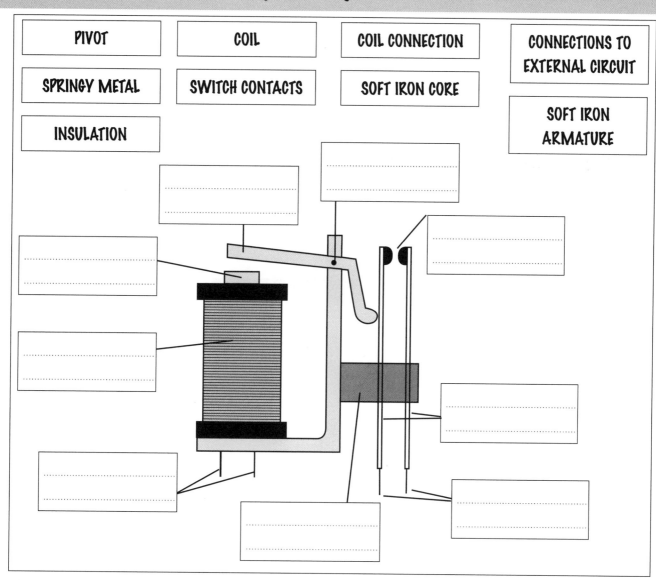

b) Explain how the relay above works.

1. The circuit shows a single pole double throw relay being used to interface a 5V control circuit to a 24V output circuit.

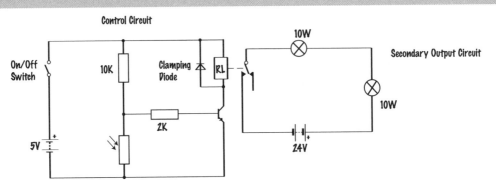

a) Explain why the output circuit is switched on in darkness.

b) What is the purpose of the clamping diode?

2. The circuit shows a double pole double throw relay being used as a latch.

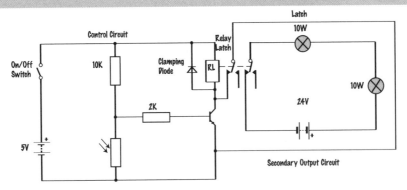

a) Explain how the above latching circuit works.

b) How would you alter the control circuit so that the output circuit is switched on in daylight?

1. Briefly explain what an integrated circuit is and what it consists of.

2. Most ICs are available as a dual in line (DIL) package. Explain what this means.

3. a) When assembling an IC on a printed circuit board (PCB) why should you always use an IC socket?

    b) Explain how you would solder an IC socket onto a PCB.

4. A 555 timer is an IC which was introduced in 1972.

    a) Give ONE use for a 555 IC in a monostable circuit.

    b) Give ONE use for a 555 IC in an astable circuit.

    c) Label the sketch of the 555 IC (above) to show Pins 1, 4 and 8. Also indicate how Pin 1 is identified.

5. The pin diagram for a 555 IC is shown below. Label it using the following:

RESET	CONTROL	DISCHARGE	THRESHOLD

OUTPUT	TRIGGER	+Vs (3V-15V)	0V

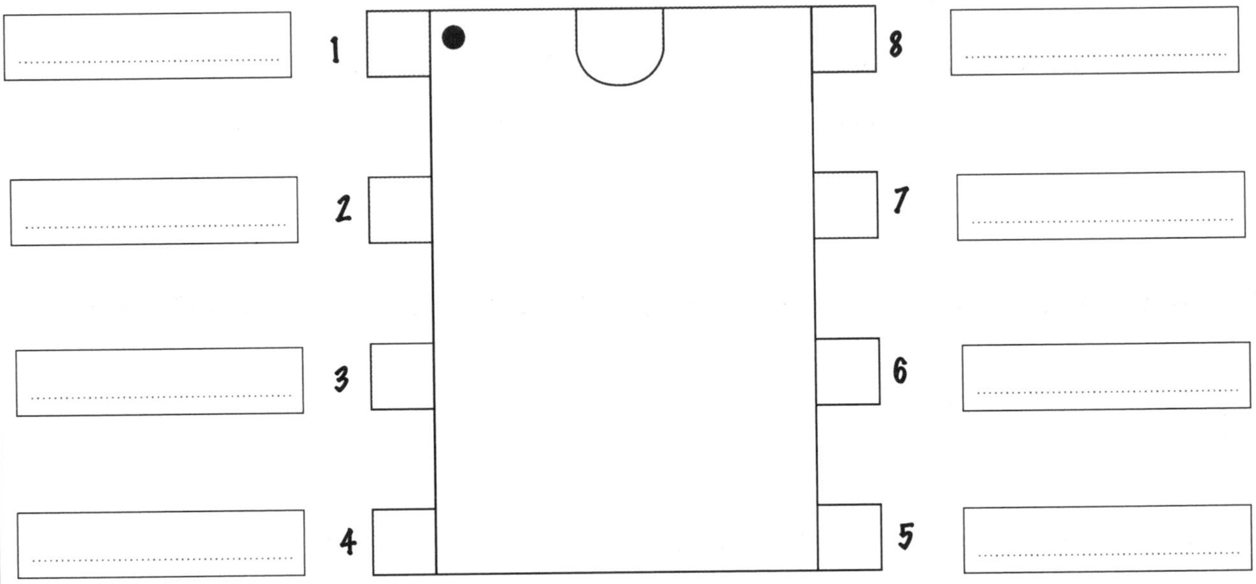

```
  [____]  1  [ ●        ⌒        ]  8  [____]

  [____]  2  [                   ]  7  [____]

  [____]  3  [                   ]  6  [____]

  [____]  4  [                   ]  5  [____]
```

6. a) When is the voltage at the output (pin 3) high?

b) When is the voltage at the output (pin 3) low?

c) Explain why the output voltage at pin 3 when high is only 7 volts even though a 9 volt battery is used to power the circuit.

d) During the operation of a 555 IC, electric current flows into or out of pin 3. Name the TWO currents and explain why we get them.

1. The circuit below shows a *555* IC being used as a monostable.

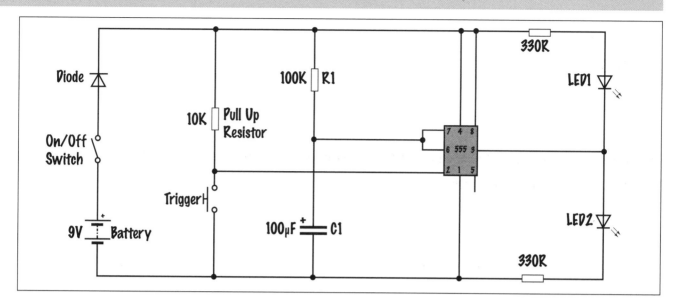

a) What is the purpose of the diode in series with the 9 volt power supply?

b) When the *555* IC is in a monostable state, is the voltage at pin 2 high or low? And is the voltage at pin 3 high or low?

Pin 2 .... Pin 3 ....

c) Explain why LED1 is lit when the *555* IC is in the monostable state.

d) What happens to the voltage at pin 2 and pin 3 when the trigger switch is pressed?

e) Explain why LED2 is now lit when the trigger switch has been pressed.

f) What is the purpose of having R1 and C1 in the circuit?

2. Calculate the time period of the 555 IC in question 1. Show your working.

Formula: ....
Working: ....
....
Answer with units: ....

3. Using your answer to question 2 draw a mark-space diagram to show the output at pin 3 if the trigger switch was pressed after 5 seconds.

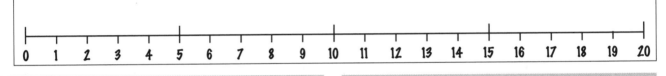

```
|       |       |       |       |       |       |
0   1   2   3   4   5   6   7   8   9   10  11  12  13  14  15  16  17  18  19  20
```

4. a) When a monostable circuit is designed the minimum value of R1 should be 1K and the minimum value of C1 should be 100pF. What time period would this monostable circuit have? Show your working.

Formula: ....
Working: ....
....
....
....
....
....
....
....
....
....
Answer with units: ....

b) When a monostable circuit is designed the maximum value of R1 should be 1M and the maximum value of C1 should be 1000µF. What time period would this monostable circuit have? Show your working.

Formula: ....
....
Working: ....
....
....
....
....
....
....
....
....
Answer with units: ....

1. The circuit below shows a 555 IC being used as an astable.

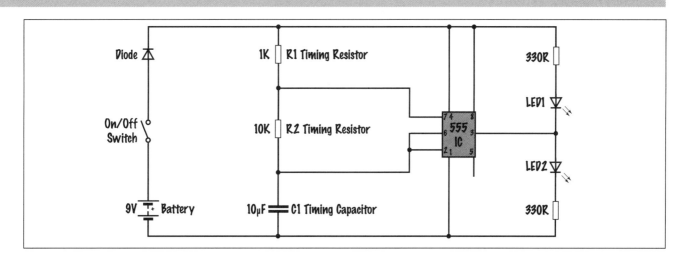

a) Why is the output voltage at pin 3 high when the circuit is first switched on?

b) Explain why LED2 lights up when the circuit is first switched on.

c) Explain why the output voltage at pin 3 changes from high to low after the circuit is first switched on.

d) Explain why LED1 lights up when the output voltage at pin 3 is low.

e) When the output voltage at pin 3 changes from high to low, capacitor C1 discharges through R2 into pin 7. Why does the output voltage at pin 3 then change from low to high and the process continually repeat until the circuit is switched off?

2. a) The number of pulses a 555 IC operating in the astable mode makes in one second is called the frequency. What is the unit of measurement for frequency?

b) Calculate the frequency of the 555 IC astable circuit in question 1. Show your working.

Formula:

Working:

Answer with units:

3. a) Why is it difficult to have an astable circuit where the output at pin 3 has an equal mark-space (on-off) ratio?

b) Suggest resistor values for R_1 and R_2 which will give an approximately equal mark-space (on-off) ratio.

c) When designing an astable circuit, why should your choice for C1 be a non-electrolytic capacitor rather than an electrolytic capacitor?

1. The circuit below shows a **555** IC monostable controlling a **555** IC astable.

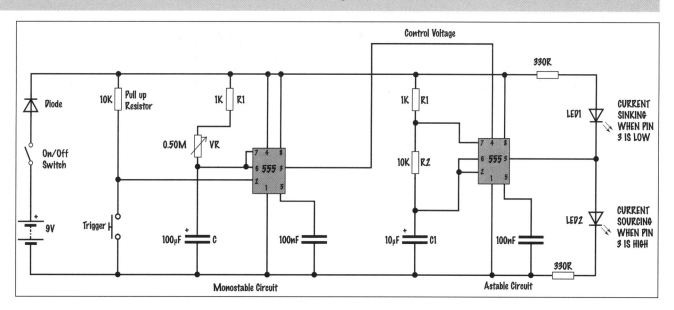

a) Explain very simply how the circuit works.

b) The variable resistor (VR) in the monostable circuit is adjustable so that the monostable circuit has a time period of **2** seconds. Draw a fully labelled mark-space ratio diagram to show what happens in the astable circuit during this time period. The trigger switch was pressed after 1 second.

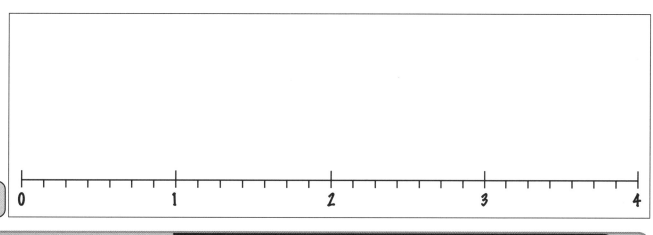

1. The pin diagram for an op-amp is shown below. Label it using the following.

| +V | OFFSET NULL | INVERTING INPUT | OV OR −V |
| NON-INVERTING INPUT | OFFSET NULL | NO CONNECTION | OUTPUT |

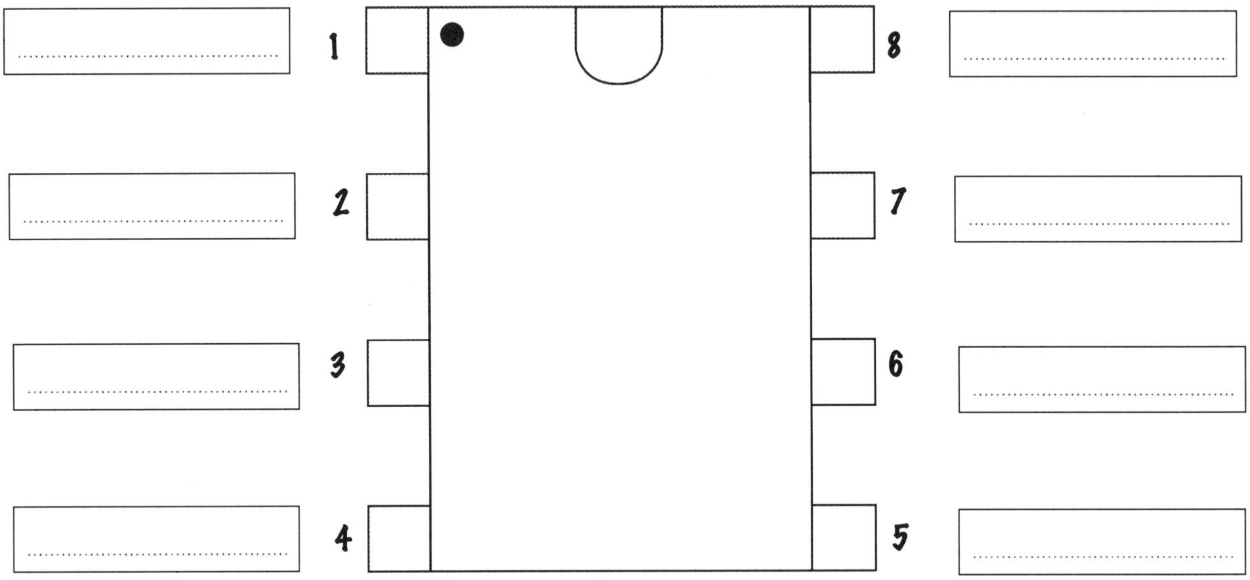

.... 1   8 ....

.... 2   7 ....

.... 3   6 ....

.... 4   5 ....

2. How many inputs and outputs does an op-amp have?

Inputs: .... Outputs: ....

3. Explain, using a diagram, how you would connect two PP3 batteries to provide a dual power supply of +9 volts, 0 volts and −9 volts

1. a) Are the following statements about the op-amp TRUE or FALSE?

i) The output of an op-amp is high voltage if the inverting input voltage is bigger than the non-inverting input voltage.

ii) The output of an op-amp is low voltage if the non-inverting input voltage is smaller than the inverting input voltage.

iii) The op-amp can only detect large changes in voltage between the inverting and non-inverting inputs.

iv) The output of an op-amp is low voltage if the inverting input voltage is smaller than the non-inverting input voltage.

v) The output of an op-amp is high voltage if the non-inverting input voltage is bigger than the inverting input voltage.

b) Complete the following table. The first one has been done for you.

PIN 2	PIN 3	PIN 6
INVERTING INPUT VOLTAGE	NON-INVERTING INPUT VOLTAGE	OUTPUT VOLTAGE
4V	3V	low
3V	4V	
3.3V	2.2V	
3.03V	3.3V	
4.10V	4.01V	
6.01V	5.99V	

2. Give TWO disadvantages of using a 741 op-amp rather than a 3140 FET op-amp.

i)

ii)

1. The circuit below shows an op-amp being used as a comparator.

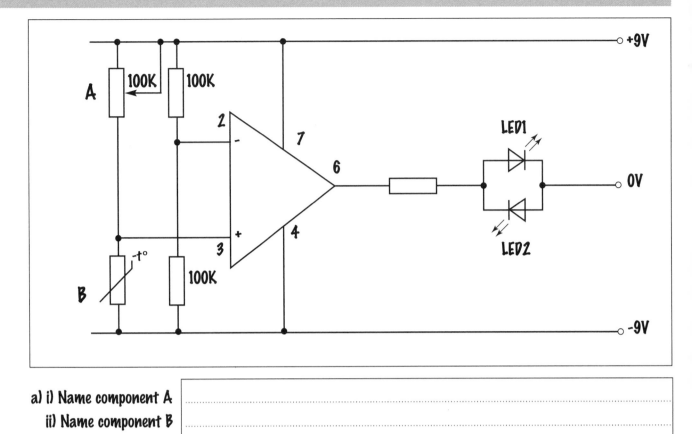

a) i) Name component A

....

   ii) Name component B

....

b) Explain what happens to the voltage on pin 3 as the temperature around component B changes.

....
....
....

c) To begin with, the voltage input to pin 2 is slightly greater than the voltage input to pin 3. Explain, giving reasons, whether LED1 or LED2 will be lit.

....
....
....
....

d) What must now happen to the temperature around component B to change which LED is lit? Explain your answer.

....
....
....
....

1. a) Approximately what is the gain of an op-amp in an open loop?

    b) Why is this gain sometimes unwanted?

    c) What is meant by negative feedback?

    d) What are the advantages of negative feedback?

2. The diagram shows an op-amp being used as an inverting amplifier. a) Complete the table below.

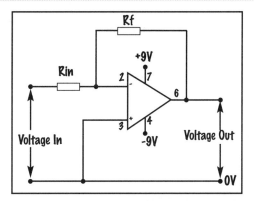

	R$_f$	R$_{in}$	GAIN	VOLTAGE IN	VOLTAGE OUT
i)	20K	10K	....	1 volt	....
ii)	....	15K	-5	....	-2.5 volts
iii)	27K	....	-1	5 volts	....
iv)	....	12K	....	0.5 volts	5 volts
v)	470K	47K	....	2 volts	....
vi)	390K	130K	....	....	3.3 volts

    b) Which of the above would result in clipping? Explain your choice.

1. The diagram below shows an op-amp operating as a voltage comparator.

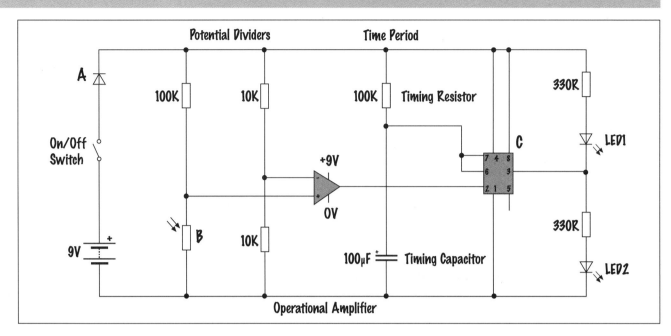

a) Name the components:

i) A .... ii) B .... iii) C ....

b) Is component C being used as a monostable or an astable? [..]

c) In darkness the resistance of component B is about 10M and in bright light its resistance is about 1K.
i) What is the output voltage of the op-amp in darkness?

ii) What would be the voltage at pin 3 of component C?

iii) Would LED1 or LED2 be lit? Explain your choice.

d) Explain very simply why the other LED would be lit when component B is exposed to bright light.

1. Explain, using diagrams, the difference between an analogue signal and a digital signal.

2. Logic gates are digital electronic devices. Explain why they cannot cope with inputs that are analogue.

3. Complete the following table.

NAME OF GATE	SYMBOL	TRUTH TABLE
....		<table><tr><td>A</td><td>Q</td></tr><tr><td>1</td><td>0</td></tr><tr><td>0</td><td>1</td></tr></table>
....	A ——⟩ B ——⟩ Q	<table><tr><td>A</td><td>B</td><td>Q</td></tr><tr><td>0</td><td>0</td><td></td></tr><tr><td>0</td><td>1</td><td></td></tr><tr><td>1</td><td>0</td><td></td></tr><tr><td>1</td><td>1</td><td></td></tr></table>
Two-input AND		<table><tr><td>A</td><td>B</td><td>Q</td></tr><tr><td>0</td><td>0</td><td></td></tr><tr><td>0</td><td>1</td><td></td></tr><tr><td>1</td><td>0</td><td></td></tr><tr><td>1</td><td>1</td><td></td></tr></table>

4. a) What similarities are there between the two-input AND gate and the two-input OR gate?

b) What differences are there between the two-input AND gate and the two-input OR gate?

5. a) i) In the space below draw the symbol and complete the truth table for a two-input NAND gate.

LOGIC DIAGRAM	TRUTH TABLE		
	A	B	Q
	0	0	
	0	1	
	1	0	
	1	1	

ii) A NAND gate means NOT AND. Explain what this means.

....

b) i) In the space below draw and label the symbol and complete the truth table for a two-input NOR gate.

LOGIC DIAGRAM	TRUTH TABLE		
	A	B	Q
	0	0	
	0	1	
	1	0	
	1	1	

ii) A NOR gate means NOT OR. Explain what this means.

....

c) i) In the space below draw and label the symbol and complete the truth table for a two-input EXCLUSIVE OR (XOR) gate.

LOGIC DIAGRAM	TRUTH TABLE		
	A	B	Q
	0	0	
	0	1	
	1	0	
	1	1	

ii) Explain why the EXCLUSIVE OR gate was developed from the OR gate.

....
....

1. Why is the NAND logic gate often referred to as the universal building block?

....

2. Complete the following table using only NAND gates.

<table>
<tr><th>NAME OF GATE</th><th>LOGIC DIAGRAM</th><th>TRUTH TABLE</th></tr>
<tr><td>NOT</td><td></td><td></td></tr>
<tr><td>..............................</td><td>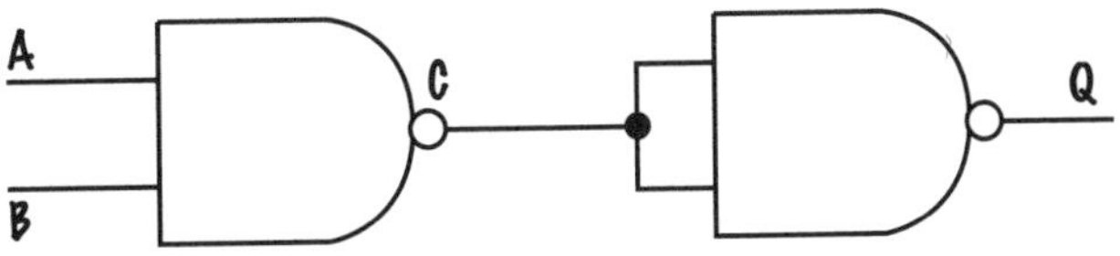
</td><td></td></tr>
<tr><td>..............................</td><td></td><td>
<table>
<tr><th>A</th><th>B</th><th>C</th><th>D</th><th>Q</th></tr>
<tr><td>0</td><td>0</td><td>1</td><td>1</td><td>0</td></tr>
<tr><td>0</td><td>1</td><td>1</td><td>0</td><td>1</td></tr>
<tr><td>1</td><td>0</td><td>0</td><td>1</td><td>1</td></tr>
<tr><td>1</td><td>1</td><td>0</td><td>0</td><td>1</td></tr>
</table>
</td></tr>
<tr><td>NOR</td><td></td><td></td></tr>
<tr><td>..............................</td><td>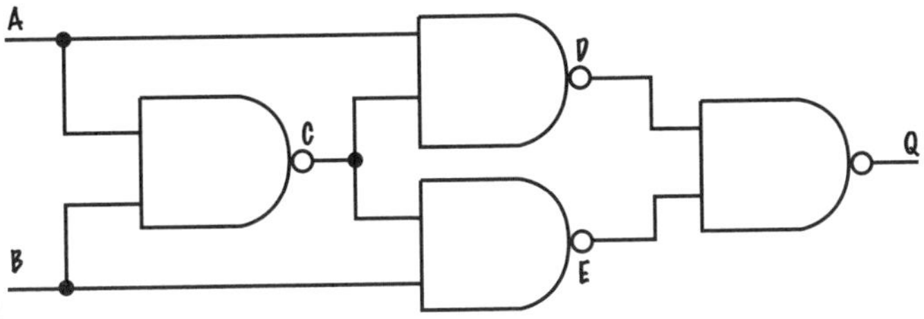
</td><td></td></tr>
</table>

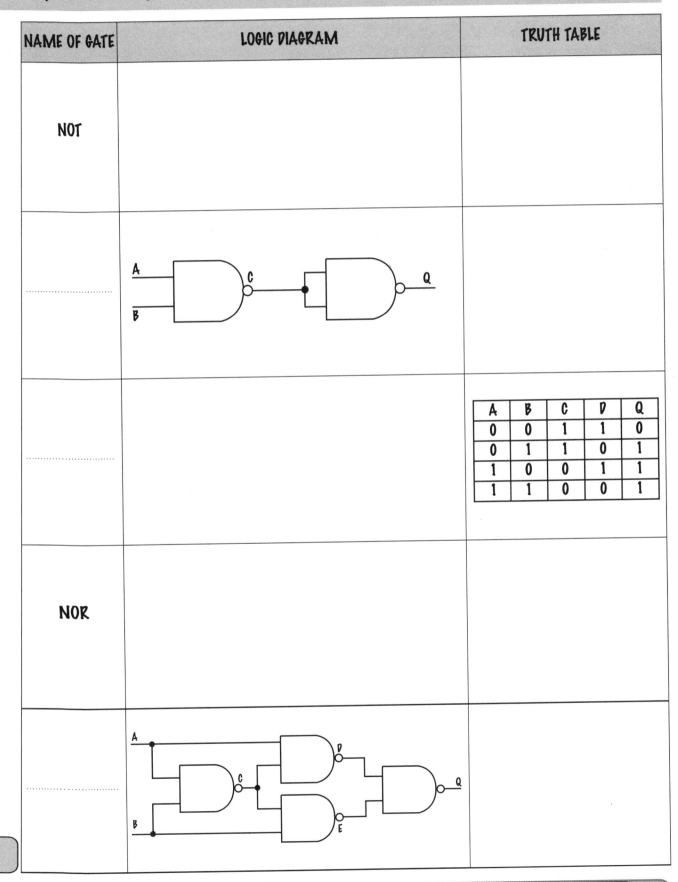

1. a) Draw an astable circuit made from two NAND gates, a fixed resistor and a non-electrolytic capacitor.

b) Suggest component values for the resistor and the capacitor.

2. a) Draw a time delay circuit made from two NAND gates, a fixed resistor and an electrolytic capacitor.

b) i) Explain what is meant by the term 'threshold level'.

ii) Suggest a threshold value if the circuit is powered by a 9V battery.

3. a) Draw an electronic latch circuit made from two NAND gates and a fixed resistor.

b) Explain how the circuit works and indicate, using arrows, the direction of feedback.

1. The pin diagram of a 4017 IC is shown below. Label it using the following:

+ Vs (3V–15V)	OUTPUT 4	OUTPUT 8	ENABLE
OUTPUT 2	OUTPUT 6	CLOCK	OUTPUT 1
DIVIDE BY 10 OUTPUT	RESET	OUTPUT 3	OUTPUT 5
OUTPUT 0	OUTPUT 7	OUTPUT 9	0V

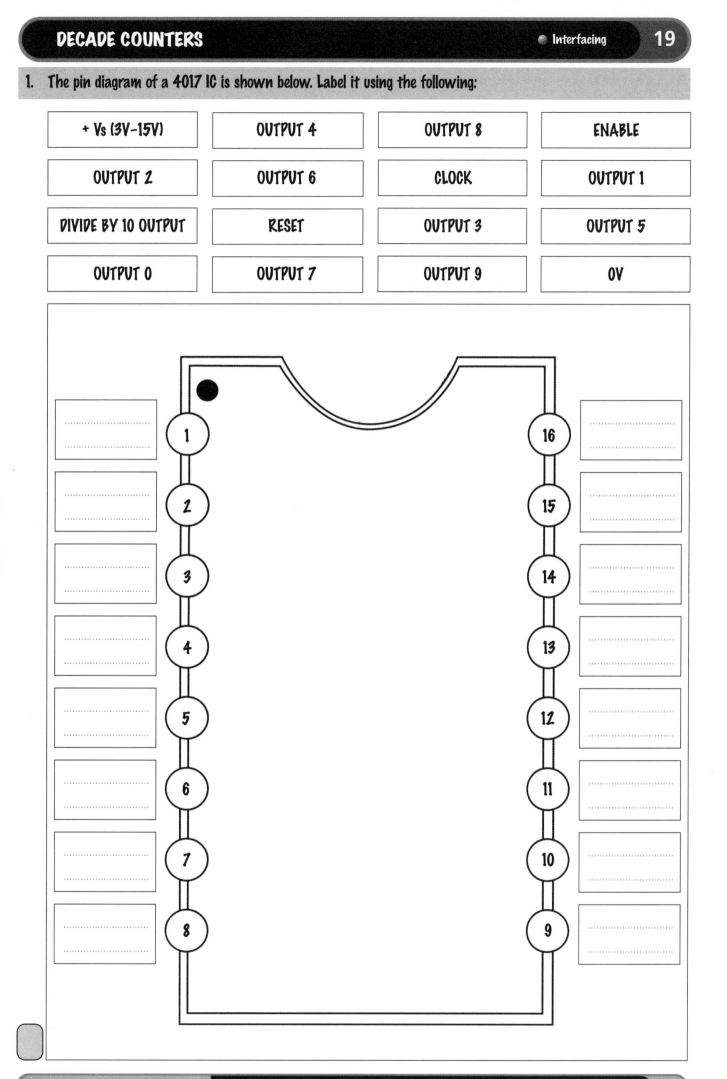

1. Explain what is meant by the term 'switch bounce' when using mechanical switches.

2. a) In the space below draw TWO ways of overcoming switch bounce in electronic circuits.

i)

ii)

b) Explain how the circuits work.

i)

ii)

1. Peripheral interface controllers (PICs) are sometimes referred to by different names. Give TWO alternative names.

   i) ....

   ii) ....

2. What is a PIC microcontroller?

   ....

   ....

3. Why are PICs often referred to as the computer in a chip?

   ....

   ....

4. PIC microcontrollers are used in all types of consumer goods. List FIVE products which may include a PIC as part of their electronic circuitry.

   i) ....

   ii) ....

   iii) ....

   iv) ....

   v) ....

5. What are the advantages of using a PIC microcontroller to replace an electronic circuit consisting of discrete components and integrated circuits?

   ....

   ....

   ....

6. Explain these terms:

   a) Flash reprogrammable. ....

   ....

   ....

   b) One-time reprogrammable. ....

   ....

   ....

7. PIC microcontrollers are manufactured in a range of pin sizes. List FOUR.

i) .... ii) ....

iii) .... iv) ....

8. PIC microcontrollers are available in a dual in line (DIL) package. Draw an 8 pin PIC to illustrate what is meant by 'dual in line'. Indicate on your drawing how pin 1 is identified and label pins 1 and 8.

9. What is the supply voltage range of a PIC microcontroller?

....

10. Explain how you would make a supply voltage range of 4.5V.

....

....

....

11. Explain how you would make a supply voltage of 5.3V.

....

....

....

1. Name TWO low level programming languages.

i) .... ii) ....

2. What are the advantages and disadvantages of low level programming language?

Advantages: ....

Disadvantages: ....

3. Name TWO high level programming languages.

i) .... ii) ....

4. What are the advantages and disadvantages of high level programming language?

Advantages: ....

Disadvantages: ....

5. What do the letters in 'BASIC' stand for?

....

6. Draw the flow chart symbols for:

Terminator

Decision

Process

Input/Output

7. What is the difference between the decimal system of counting and the binary system of counting?

8. Complete the binary table below. The first and last lines have been done for you.

MSB			LSB	DECIMAL
0	0	0	0	0
				1
				2
				3
				4
				5
				6
				7
1	0	0	0	8

9. a) What does 'LSB' stand for?

b) What does 'MSB' stand for?

10. a) Convert the binary number 1101 to decimal.

b) Convert the decimal number 14 to binary.

11. A list of the operations when using a PIC is shown below, but they are not in the correct order. Complete the block diagram using the letters A, B, C and D to give the correct order of operations when using PIC microprocessors. Block E has been done for you.

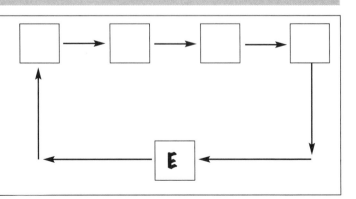

A Download onto PIC
B Insert PIC into final working circuit and
   test
C Design flow chart or BASIC programme
   using a computer
D Test the procedure on screen
E Flash erase flow chart of BASIC programme